www.raintreepublishers.co.uk
Visit our website to find out
more information about
Raintree books.

To order:
☎ Phone 0845 6044371
📠 Fax +44 (0) 1865 312263
✉ Email myorders@raintreepublishers.co.uk

Customers from outside the UK please telephone +44 1865 312262

Raintree is an imprint of
Capstone Global Library Limited, a
company incorporated in England
and Wales having its registered
office at 7 Pilgrim Street, London,
EC4V 6LB - Registered company
number: 6695582

First published by Raintree in 2013
The moral rights of the proprietor have been asserted.

Originally published by DC Comics in the U.S. in single
magazine form as Superman Adventures #2.
Copyright © 2012 DC Comics. All Rights Reserved.

Ashley C. Andersen Zantop *Publisher*
Michael Dahl *Editorial Director*
Donald Lemke & Sean Tulien *Editors*
Heather Kindseth *Creative Director*
Bob Lentz *Designer*
Kathy McColley *Production Specialist*

DC COMICS
Mike McAvennie *Original U.S. Editor*
Bruce Timm *Cover Artist*

ISBN 978 1 406 25400 6
19 18 17 16 15
10 9 8 7 6 5 4 3
Printed and bound in China.

British Library Cataloguing in Publication Data
A full catalogue record for this book is available
from the British Library.

SUPERMAN ADVENTURES

Be Careful What You Wish For

Scott McCloud...................... writer
Rick Burchett ....penciller
Terry Austin .... inker
Marie Severin .... colorist
Lois Buhalis........................ letterer

Superman created by
Jerry Siegel & Joe Shuster

SUPERMAN! HELP!!

Be Careful What You Wish For...

SCOTT McCLOUD - WRITER
RICK BURCHETT - PENCILLER
TERRY AUSTIN - INKER
MARIE SEVERIN - COLORIST
LOIS BUHALIS - LETTERER
MIKE McAVENNIE - EDITOR

SUPERMAN
CREATED BY
JERRY SIEGEL AND
JOE SHUSTER

WHAT?! WHAT'S WRONG?!

≠Gasp!≠

MISS, WHAT'S WRONG? ARE YOU IN DANGER?

UH--

UH--

UH, ACTUALLY, I--

UH--

I JUST W-WANTED TO MEET YOU.

SORRY.

SO, UM... CAN I HAVE YOUR AUTOGRAPH?

Sigh I'M SORRY, I HAVE TO GO.

THAT'S THE THIRD TIME THIS MORNING.

BOY, WHAT A GROUCH!

THANKS FOR THE FLOWERS, HONEY!

I HOPE NO ONE HEARD THAT.

SUPERMAN! THE MAN OF STEEL! WHO IS HE? WHERE DID HE COME FROM?

ALL OF METROPOLIS IS *BUZZING* STILL WITH THE NEWS OF THIS INCREDIBLE HERO FROM ANOTHER WORLD.

THOUGH ONLY IN TOWN A FEW MONTHS, SUPERMAN'S *SUPER-STRENGTH* HAS FOILED *CRIME AFTER CRIME*, DEFEATED A COLORFUL ARRAY OF POWERFUL OPPONENTS, AND WON FANS THE WORLD OVER!

STILL, MOST OF US ARE TOO *DAZZLED* TO DOUBT!

SOME SAY IT'S ALL A *HOAX*, AND ASK WHY SUPER-BEINGS LIKE TOYMAN, THE PARASITE OR METALLO, "THE KILLER WITH THE KRYPTO-NITE HEART," ONLY CAME ON THE SCENE WHEN THERE WAS SOMEONE STRONG ENOUGH TO *CHALLENGE* THEM.

BUT QUESTIONS ABOUND! WHERE DO HIS POWERS COME FROM? WHY IS HE HERE ON EARTH?

WHAT MAKES THAT *SUPER-BOD* OF HIS TICK? AND IS THERE A SUPER-MISS WE DON'T KNOW ABOUT?

I'M ANGELA CHEN, AND TODAY WE GO UP CLOSE AND PERSONAL, OR AT LEAST AS CLOSE AS WE CAN GET TO--

SHUT THAT THING OFF, WILL YOU, JIMMY?

KENT, YOU'RE **LATE!**

SORRY, Mr. WHITE.

LOOK, YOU'RE THE ONLY CONTACT I *HAVE* IN HIS HOME TOWN. YOU'VE *GOT* TO HELP ME GET THE *DIRT* ON THIS GUY.

IF WE CAN GET EVIDENCE OF A *CONSPIRACY,* WE CAN BREAK THIS THING *WIDE OPEN!*

LOIS, I'VE GOT--

LISTEN, I WANT *NAMES.* I WANT *DATES.*

IT SHOULDN'T TAKE YOU LONG--HOW ABOUT *TOMORROW MORNING?*

TOMORROW *AFTERNOON.* RIGHT. *UH-HUH. UH-HUH. EXACTLY.*

LOIS, WE--

WHAT?

≶*Sigh*≷ I LOVE YOU, *TOO,* MOM. BYE-BYE.

WHAT IS IT, *SMALL-VILLE?*

I'VE GOT A SOURCE LINED UP FOR THOSE *WHARF ROBBERIES.* HE'S YOURS--FOR A *SHARED BYLINE.*

DONE, KENT. DID YOU SEE THE *HEADLINE* THIS MORNING? MY *DMV SCANDAL* STORY GOT *BUMPED* TO PAGE THREE! DOES THAT SEEM *RIGHT* TO YOU?

I MEAN, WHAT DID SUPERMAN *DO,* REALLY? JUST--

--SAVE TWENTY MILLION PEOPLE?

HOB'S BAY

♪

324

HEY, SOL, GIMME A PRETZEL.

HEY, KELLY. WAS THAT REALLY *SUPERMAN* I SAW FLYING OUT OF YOUR WINDOW THIS MORNING?

SOL'S PRETZEL'S 'R' US

AW, ACTUALLY, HE, *UH*... ...*UH, YEAH.* YEAH, I GUESS YOU COULD SAY WE'RE KIND OF *AN ITEM.*

WOW!

HEY, THAT'S *SUPERMAN'S GIRLFRIEND!*

DON'T *SPREAD IT AROUND* TOO MUCH, SOL!

PRETZELS 1.50
CHIPS 1.00
SODER 1.25
COOKIES 1.7⁵

DAILY PLANET

HEY, BIRD...

LOOKS LIKE I WON'T BE GETTING THAT JOB. TURNS OUT THEY WANT SOMEONE WITH MORE *EXPERIENCE.*

BOY, I GUESS THIS ISN'T WORKING OUT SO WELL.

I THOUGHT FOR *SURE* IF I STAYED IN *METROPOLIS* AFTER SCHOOL. THAT THINGS WOULD JUST KICK INTO *HIGH GEAR.*

NOTHING EXCITING IS *EVER* GOING TO HAPPEN TO ME.

I SHOULD'VE NEVER LEFT *TOPEKA.*

BUT *HEY,* I'M *SUPERMAN'S* GIRL NOW! YEAH...

"WHY, *SUPERMAN,* HOW *NICE* OF YOU TO *DROP BY.* I--"

ONE WORD...

...AND YOU'RE *DEAD*.

THREE NIGHTS IN A ROW WE'VE BEEN LOSING INVENTORY. *ASSAULT RIFLES*, MOSTLY. *CLIPS*. SOME *BIGGER STUFF*.

DOESN'T MATTER WHAT KINDA *SECURITY* WE PUT ON IT. EACH TIME THEY SMASH RIGHT THROUGH A *DIFFERENT WALL*, GRAB THE STUFF AND *TAKE OFF* BEFORE ANYONE CAN SEE 'EM.

IT'S LIKE THEY AREN'T EVEN *HUMAN!*

FLEISCHE IMPORT EXPORT

SO LAST NIGHT I GET A CALL FROM ONE OF MY GUARDS. SEZ HE SAW SOME SHADY GUYS DOING A DEAL NEARBY ON HIS WAY HOME AND TRACKED THIS *ONE GUY* TO A *GREEN HOUSEBOAT*.

I TOLD HIM TO CALL THE COPS, BUT I GUESS HE WENT AFTER THE GUY HIMSELF, AND...

...AND YOU HAVEN'T SEEN HIM SINCE. SOUNDS LIKE AN OLD "FRIEND" OF OURS, DOESN'T IT, *KENT?*

HMM...

I DON'T *KNOW*, LOIS. WHY WOULD CORBEN GO BACK TO *GUN-RUNNING?*

WHAT WOULD HE USE THE *MONEY* FOR, NOW THAT HE'S BECOME *METALLO?*

WELL, I'LL GRANT YOU, THEY NEVER FOUND THE *BODY.* SO HE COULD STILL BE ALI--✳

MAYBE TO BUY PARTS-- FOR *HIMSELF.*

KENT?

≶HELP! SOMEBODY, HELP!≷

IT CAN'T BE *HER* AGAIN.

KENT, *SNAP OUT OF IT!*

HMM? SORRY, LOIS. I THOUGHT I *HEARD* SOMETHING.

WELL, STAY *ALERT.* WE'VE GOT A LOT OF *GREEN HOUSEBOATS* TO VISIT.

13

OH, THERE'S BEEN A MISTAKE, ALL RIGHT. YOUR *BOYFRIEND* MADE THE BIGGEST MISTAKE OF HIS *LIFE* WHEN HE TOOK ME ON!

THANKS TO SUPERMAN AND LEX LUTHOR, I'M STUCK IN THIS BLASTED *TIN CAN* FOR *LIFE*!

BOYFRIEND--?

OH, *HA-HA!* HE'S NOT MY *BOYFRIEND*, I JUST--

DON'T WASTE YOUR *BREATH*, SWEETIE. I KNOW *EXACTLY* WHAT YOU ARE. YOU'RE THE *BAIT*, SUPERMAN IS THE *FISH*--

--AND *HERE'S* WHAT I'M GONNA *FRY* HIM WITH! *HA-HA-HA!*

Gasp! IS THAT K-KR--?

KRYPTONITE IT IS, AND--

KNOCK KNOCK

WHO IN HADES--?

GET LOST!

NOW *THAT'S* WHAT I LIKE TO HEAR!

CORBEN, IS THAT YOU? THIS IS LOIS LANE, DAILY PLANET.

LOIS, MAYBE WE SHOULD CALL THE POLI--

--IS TOAST!

AAAAGH!

HA·HA·HA!

N-NO...

WHY SO UPSET, DARLING?

OH, OF COURSE! YOU WANT TO JOIN HIM!

GET READY FOR IT, HONEY. YOU'RE ABOUT TO--

WHAT THE DEVIL ARE YOU STARING AT?

L-L--

L-LOOK!

SOON...

SO, KELLY, A LITTLE BIRD TELLS ME YOU'RE SUPERMAN'S GIRLFRIEND!

NOW, WAIT A MIN--

NO WAY! UH-UH! NOT ME, LADY!

BUT KELLY, YOU SAID YOU WERE!

YOU SAID YOU WERE SUPERMAN'S GIRLFRIEND!

WELL, YEAH, BUT, UH...

UH... ...HE WAS, 'TIL, UH...

...'TIL, UH...

SLAP!

I WAS UNTIL I SAW HIM WITH--

--WITH HER!

WHAT?!?

SORRY! GOTTA GO!

MISS LANE! WOW!

LOIS! ANY COMMENT FOR--?

NOW HOLD ON ONE MIN--!

ANGELA, IF YOU AIR THAT, I SWEAR I'LL--

AH, FICKLENESS, THY NAME IS LOVE!

THE END

CREATORS

SCOTT McCLOUD — WRITER

Scott McCloud is an acclaimed comics creator and author whose best-known work is the graphic novel *Understanding Comics*. His work also includes the science-fiction adventure series *Zot!*, a 12-issue run of *Superman Adventures*, and much more. Scott is the creator of the "24 Hour Comic," and frequently lectures on comics theory.

RICK BURCHETT — PENCILLER

Rick Burchett has worked as a comics artist for more than 25 years. He has received the comics industry's Eisner Award three times, Spain's Haxtur Award, and he has been nominated for England's Eagle Award. Rick lives with his wife and two sons in Missouri, USA.

TERRY AUSTIN — INKER

Throughout his career, inker Terry Austin has received dozens of awards for his work on high-profile comics for DC Comics and Marvel, such as *The Uncanny X-Men*, *Doctor Strange*, *Justice League America*, *Green Lantern*, and *Superman Adventures*. He lives in New York, USA.

GLOSSARY

alert if you are alert, you pay attention to what is happening and are ready for action

array large number of things

chivalrous if someone is chivalrous, they are polite and helpful, especially a man toward a woman

conspiracy secret, illegal plan made by two or more people

evidence information and facts that help prove something

experience knowledge and skill you gain by doing something

fickleness someone who is fickle changes their mind often

hesitate to pauses before doing something

hoax trick or practical joke

scoop big story, or the first report of a story in a news

shady shady person is someone who is sneaky or not trustworthy

wharf long dock, built along a shore, where boats and ships can load and unload

SUPERMAN GLOSSARY

Clark Kent: Superman's alter ego, Clark Kent, is a reporter for the *Daily Planet* newspaper and was raised by Ma and Pa Kent. No one knows he is Superman except for his adopted parents, the Kents.

The Daily Planet: the city of Metropolis's biggest and most read newspaper. Clark, Lois, Jimmy, and Perry all work for the *Daily Planet*.

Invulnerability: Superman's invulnerability makes him impervious to harm. Almost nothing can hurt him -- except for Kryptonite, a radioactive rock from his home planet, Krypton.

Jimmy Olsen: Jimmy is a cub reporter and photographer. He is also a friend to Lois and Clark.

The Kent Family: Ma and Pa Kent found Superman when he crashed to Earth from his home planet, Krypton. They raised him as their own child, giving him the name Clark.

Lex Luthor: Lex believes Superman is a threat to Earth and must be stopped. He will do anything it takes to bring the Man of Steel to his knees.

Lois Lane: like Clark Kent, Lois is a reporter at the *Daily Planet* newspaper. She is also one of Clark's best friends.

Metropolis: the city where Clark Kent (Superman) lives.

Super-strength: one of Superman's most important superpowers is his ability to exert tremendous force using his powerful muscles.

1. The title of this comic book is *Be Careful What You Wish For*. Based on this young woman's interactions with the Man of Steel, what do you think the book title means? What did she wish for? How did the experience turn out for her?

2. This single scene of action is broken into three individual panels. Identify what the focus is of each panel. Why do you think the artist decided to break up the scene like this?

3. Clark Kent is secretly Superman. What kinds of things would make it difficult to be two different people like Clark and the Man of Steel? What advantages and disadvantages are there?

4. In the panel below, who do you think Clark Kent called? Explain.

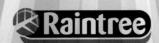